Featuring:
Rawli Davis
Corey Fayman
The La Jolla Bowl
The Pink Poodle
Mark Baber
A Horse
Miramar Naval Air Station
U.S. Marine Corps Training Depot, San Diego
George Pernicano's Pizza House
And many others.

Do you know what I'm going to do Next Saturday?

by Helen Palmer

with photographs by
Lynn Fayman

BOOK CLUB EDITION

BEGINNER BOOKS   A Division of Random House, Inc.

© Copyright, 1963, by Helen Palmer. All rights reserved under International and Pan-American Copyright Conventions. Published in New York by Beginner Books, a division of Random House, Inc., and simultaneously in Toronto, Canada, by Random House of Canada, Limited. Library of Congress Catalog Card Number: 63-17572. Manufactured in the United States of America.

Do you know what I'm going to do next Saturday? Well, sir . . . . . I'm going to do some things no one ever did before.

First of all,
I'm going to eat
a big, big breakfast.
Next Saturday is going to be
a big, big day.

Next Saturday . . . wow!

I'm going to do some tricks

no one ever saw before.

I'm going to dive
some dives no one
ever dived before.

Yes, sir!

8

That is the kind of thing
I'm going to do next Saturday.

Did you ever beat
more than one kid at a time?

Well, I'm going to beat
five kids at a time.

And then I'm going to beat
their fathers, too.
Saturday is going to be
my big, big day.

After that,

I'll eat a little something.

You have to keep eating

if you want to keep going.

And next Saturday

I'm going to go a long, long way.

On Saturday I'm going to do
everything I want to do.
I'm going to go bowling
if I want to.

Then I'm going to
ski on water
if I want to.

And I want to.

Then I'm going to dive down
to the bottom of the sea.
I'm going to do everything.
No one can stop me.

I'm going to go
up high
if I want to.
And I want to.

I'm going to find someone
to take me up in a jet.

Did you ever go up in a jet?
Well, I'm going to next Saturday.
No kid in town ever did
a thing like that before.

But I'll do more than that.

Did you ever go up

in a heli . . heli . . heli . .

How do you say it?

Helicopter is how you say it.

Well, sir,

I'm going to go up

in a helicopter, too.

Then I'll come down.
I'll dump water on Sam.
I'll make him take a walk.
I'll make Sam walk
about a hundred miles.

After a walk like that,

I'll have to eat a little something.

Sam won't keep going,

but I want to keep going.

So I'll have to eat and eat.

Next Saturday
I'm going to
eat like a horse.

I'm going to jump more stumps
than anyone ever jumped before.
Everything I do will be fun!
Yes, everything!

Everything . . .? Well . . .
Maybe not everything.
There is one thing I don't
want to do next Saturday.

Mother told me
I'll have to get my hair cut.

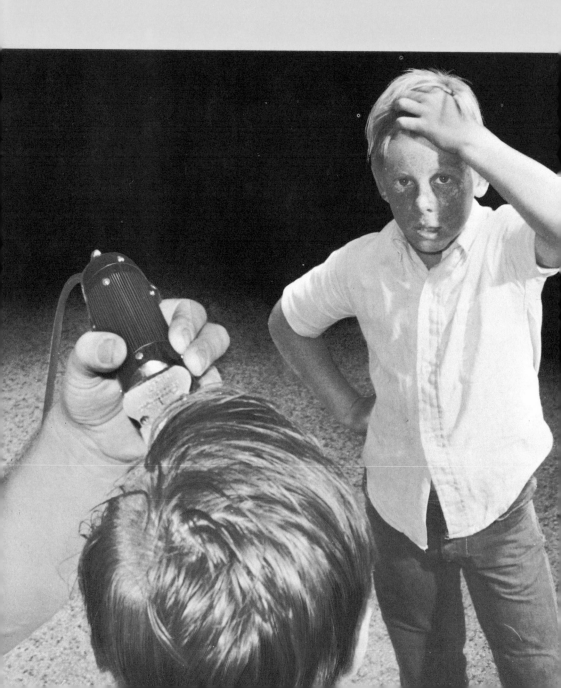

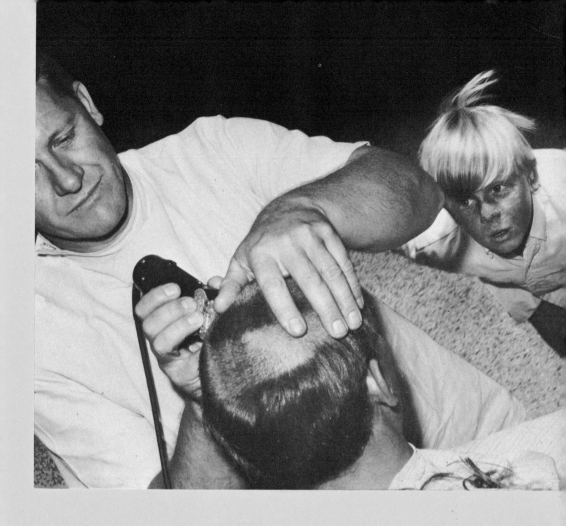

All right.

I'll go.

I'll go

and look things over.

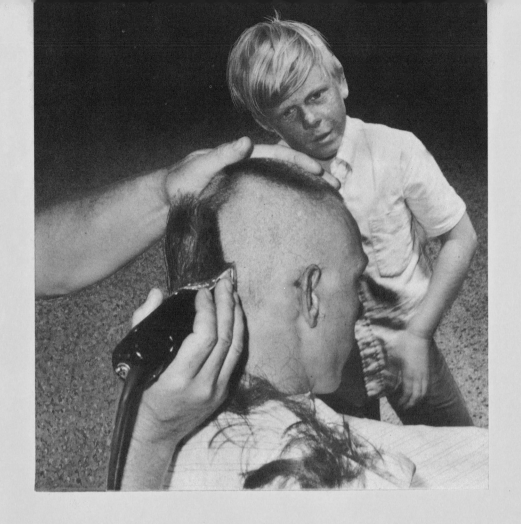

Oh! Oh!

Do I want to look

like that next Saturday?

No, sir! No, sir!
Not next Saturday.

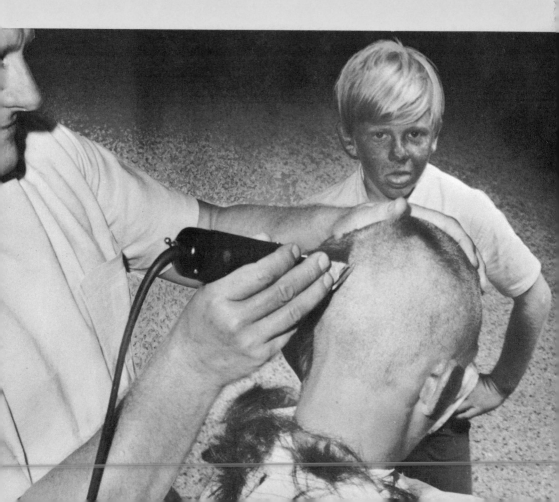

I'll get out of there fast,
and I'll take my hair with me.
No one is going to stop me
next Saturday.

There are things I want to do.

Did you ever play

with the United States Marines?

Shooting!

I'll go shooting

with the United States Marines.

Little guns! Big guns!
I'll shoot every gun
that they shoot.

The Marines will like my shooting.
And they are going to like me.

They will ask
me to stay
and eat a little
something.
You have to keep eating
if you want to keep going.

I'll stay with them.
I'll play with them.
I'll run with them.
I'll race with them.

Did you ever box

a United States Marine?

Well, sir, I'm going to box

a Marine next Saturday.

Then I'll box another way.

I'll box with sticks.

Two Marines at a time!

No kid ever, ever did

a thing like that before.

I'll do everything,
everything, everything they do.
I'll be fast next Saturday.
I'm going to beat them all.

I'll beat them.
Then I'll leave them.
I have other things to do. . . .

I'll run around and yell and yell.
Next Saturday I'll yell my head off.
I'll blow horns. I'll blow and blow.
Next Saturday I'll blow my head off.

No one is going
to stop me
next Saturday.

They will try to stop me.
They may catch me.
They may take me away
in a big tin can.
They may dump me
over a wall.

But I'll pop up again.

And then
do you know what I'm going to do?

Well, sir,
let me tell you . . .

I'm going to eat
more spaghetti
than anyone
ever ate before.

Did you ever eat

a mile of spaghetti?

Did you ever eat

two miles of spaghetti?

Well, sir . . .

I'm going to eat

TEN MILES OF SPAGHETTI.

No one ever, ever

did that before.

Not even a United States Marine!

So . . .

when the Marines hear
about me and all that spaghetti,
do you know what they will do?

They will put on a parade.

A parade just for me!

It will be ten miles long.

Just like the spaghetti!

Then . . .

after the parade,

I'll take them all home for supper.

I hope Mother has

a little something

in the house for us to eat.

Yes, sir!

That is what

I'm going to do next Saturday.

Saturday

is going to be

my big, big day.